# FRANKIE MORL

# World in Danger

# Foreword

When I was five, I read a book about endangered animals. I was sad that lots of wild animals might not be here when I am older.

I started a club for my friends at school, it was £1 to enter and everyone could come. We ran around our park and raised money for pandas. The charity WWF were very kind and helpful.

After doing five events I wanted to do something different, so I wrote the song "World in Danger" with my dad. I love music and sing in a choir, so writing a song was lots of fun. I hope it can make a difference to our world.

Frankie Morland

Songwriter and animal lover, aged 8

I **hope** we will be fine

I hate to see the world in **danger**

# I want to enjoy your **beauty**

## before you're **gone**

**One million** animal and plant species are at risk of **disappearing forever**.

Let's all enjoy the **world** today

Climb the **trees** and breathe the air
Let's all **enjoy** the world

Because tomorrow could be a very **different** day

6

Imagine a man sitting on the Moon

Looking down at the world

that we Created

with a **tear** in his eye

**Nine out of ten** people in the world are **breathing dirty air.**

As the grey clouds cover

his view

Let's all **enjoy** the world today

**Climb** the trees

and **breathe** the air

There may be more **plastic** in the ocean than **fish** by 2050.

Let's all enjoy the world

Because **tomorrow**

could be a very different **day**

I love to feel the
snow in the
winter

And I love to feel the
# sun in the
# spring

I love to kick the leaves that fall in autumn

**15 billion** trees are cut down every year.

And I love to enjoy the world as I sing

Let's all **enjoy**
the **world** today

18

Climb the trees
and **breathe** the air

19

# Let's all enjoy the world

Sea ice in the Arctic Ocean is **melting** faster due to **rising temperatures** across the world.

Because **tomorrow** could be a very **different** day

# Let's all **enjoy** the **world** today

## **Climb** the trees and **breathe** the air

Let's all **enjoy** the **world**

Because tomorrow could be a

**very different day**

Did you know that plastic stays around for a very long time? On landfill sites, it can take more than 400 years to break down and disappear.

# Make a T-shirt bag

Help cut down on plastic bag use by turning an old T-shirt into a handy bag.

## Step 1

Turn an old T-shirt inside out. Then, with an adult's help, carefully cut off the sleeves.

Also cut out a deep curve around the neck.

The slits should be 5 cm (2 in) long.

## Step 2

Next, cut slits at 2 cm (¾ in) intervals in a row along the bottom of the T-shirt.

## Step 3

Take the front and back strands you have just cut and double knot them all together.

Make sure your knots are tight!

## Step 4

Turn your T-shirt the right side out, and you have a new bag!

Bees are one of my favourite animals! They're important too, because they help fruit and vegetables to grow. Unfortunately, bees are disappearing across the UK.

Sedum

Snowdrop

26

# Build a bee hotel

Give your buzzy friends a place to stay by making this bee-autiful hotel from a recycled plastic bottle.

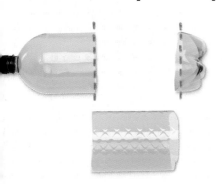

## Step 1

With the help of an adult, carefully cut both ends off a used, clean plastic bottle as shown above.

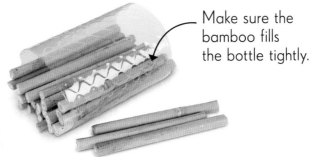

Make sure the bamboo fills the bottle tightly.

## Step 2

Get an adult to trim bamboo sticks to the same length as the bottle. Pack the bottle with the sticks.

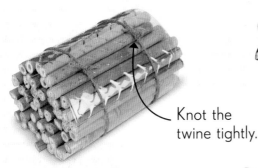

Knot the twine tightly.

## Step 3

Tie twine around both ends of the bottle.

## Step 4

Tie another piece of twine to both loops to make a handle. Hang the bee hotel 1 m (3 ft) above the ground outdoors. Then wait for the bees to visit!

Cornflower

Iris

Crocus

Lavender

27

## Elephant

Elephants are very smart and never forget a face – they can remember other elephants from more than 20 years ago!

# Frankie's favourite animals

## Penguin

When they get cold, emperor penguins snuggle together for warmth.

## Sea turtle

Sea turtles swim massive distances across the ocean, but when the time comes to lay their eggs they return to the same beach where they were born.

## Toucan

When eating, tropical toucans toss fruit up in the air with their large, rainbow-coloured beaks.

These are some of Frankie's all-time favourite animals. Sadly, most of these animals are disappearing from the wild.

## Red panda

Red pandas have amazing ankles that twist all the way round, helping them scamper up and down tree trunks.

## Lion

Female lions, called lionesses, are faster than the males and do most of the hunting. Unlike male lions, the females don't have manes.

# Now it's your turn!

Learn to play the song on guitar and piano using this handy chord sheet with lyrics.

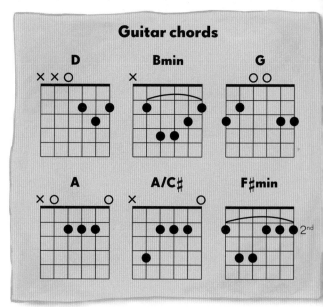

## Frankie and Charlie

Frankie naturally gravitated to music from a young age, always singing, picking up his little ukulele, playing drums, and creating lyric ideas. He wrote "World in Danger" with his dad Charlie, a musician and music tutor.

**Written by Frankie Morland**
**Illustrated by Zoë Barnish**

**Publishing Manager** Francesca Young
**Senior Commissioning Designer** Fiona Macdonald
**Managing Editor** Sam Priddy
**Editorial Assistant** Seeta Parmar
**Jacket Coordinator** Issy Walsh
**Pre-Production Producer** Abi Maxwell
**Senior Producer** Ena Matagic
**Project Picture Researcher** Sakshi Saluja
**DTP Designer** Nityanand Kumar
**Creative Director** Clare Baggaley
**Publishing Director** Sarah Larter

**Musical Score Editor and Arranger** Charlie Morland

First published in Great Britain in 2019
by Dorling Kindersley Limited
80 Strand, London, WC2R 0RL

Copyright © 2019 Dorling Kindersley Limited
A Penguin Random House Company
10 9 8 7 6 5 4 3 2 1
001–319120–Dec/2019

A CIP catalogue record for this book
is available from the British Library.
ISBN: 978-0-2414-4622-5

Printed and bound in the UK by Bell and Bain Ltd, Glasgow

A WORLD OF IDEAS:
SEE ALL THERE IS TO KNOW

www.dk.com

**DK would like to thank:** Olivia Stanford for editorial assistance and Rachael Parfitt Hunt for design assistance.

The publisher would like to thank the following for their kind permission to reproduce their photographs:
(Key: a-above; b-below/bottom; c-centre; f-far; l-left; r-right; t-top)
**28 Getty Images:** Frank Krahmer / Photographer's Choice RF (clb).
**Photolibrary:** White / Digital Zoo (tl). **29 Dreamstime.com:** Emmanuel Nalli (r).
**iStockphoto.com:** Aaprophoto (tc).

All other images © Dorling Kindersley
For further information see: www.dkimages.com